CW00864737

My name is

_____

I am_____years old

I love my **Mango** Book

Copyright © DC Books
First Published November 2008

Book Design
Design Difference, Kochi

Printed in India
Standard Press Pvt. Ltd., Sivakasi

Publisher
DC Books
21/3 Shrungar Complex, M G Road, Bangalore, Karnataka, India
D C Kizhakemuri Edam, Good Shepherd Street, Kottayam 686 001, Kerala, India
Website: www.tumbi.org
Email: editorial@tumbi.org

No portion of this book may be reproduced
or transmitted in any form or by any means
without the prior written permission of the publisher.
All rights reserved.

ISBN 978-81-264-1892-3
MANGO 0005

DC Books The first Indian Book Publishing House to get ISO Certification

SWEET WORDS OR HARSH WORDS?

RETOLD BY **ARTHY MUTHANNA SINGH**
ILLUSTRATED BY **SUDHEER P Y**

Paramsukh was a priest who once received a calf as charity. He named the calf Nandishwar and looked after him just as if he were his own son. Naturally, the calf grew up to be a strong bull.

The bull was grateful to Paramsukh for looking after him so well and wanted to repay him.

One day, he asked his master to go to the richest merchant in town and boast to him that Nandishwar could pull fifty loaded carts. Paramsukh was surprised when he heard his precious bull speak! But he listened to his advice, anyway. Nandishwar said that if the merchant did not believe him, he should place a bet for one thousand gold coins.

Paramsukh shook his head and said, "It is impossible for any bull to pull fifty loaded carts at once."

"Don't worry," said Nandishwar, "I can do it. You will become rich if you follow my instructions."

Paramsukh was worried. "What if I lose the bet?" he asked.

Nandishwar reassured him, "I am sure I can keep my promise, otherwise I would not be giving you this advice."

So, the next day, Paramsukh went to the market and walked up to the merchant.

"Can you tell me whose bull can pull the most number of loaded carts in this town?" he asked.

The merchant thought for a while and said, "I have seen many strong bulls but my bull is the strongest of them all."

Paramsukh smiled.

"Can your bull pull fifty loaded carts at one time, like my Nandishwar?" he asked.

"What rubbish!" said the merchant. "No bull can do that."

That was just the chance Paramsukh had been waiting for.

"Should we bet on that?" he asked. "I will give you one thousand gold coins if my Nandishwar does not pull fifty loaded carts at one time, and you should give me one thousand gold coins if he does. Is this a deal?"

"I agree!" shouted the merchant, who was sure he would win the bet. The men fixed the venue for the challenge on the outskirts of the town.

That evening, Paramsukh was ready with fifty carts loaded with sand and stones. He was happy, but also nervous. "I will soon have so much money," he thought. "Then I will buy more bulls and bet again. Soon, I will be the richest man in town... I should make sure Nandishwar wins the bet."

So, when the merchant came to the spot, Paramsukh put the yoke on Nadishwar's neck, climbed on to the first cart and started whipping him. "Come on!" he shouted. "What are you waiting for? Move, you silly bull! Hurry up!"

Nandishwar was shocked. He could not believe that his loving master had whipped him! And why was he being so rude and using abusive language? Nandishwar was hurt. He decided not to move an inch.

What could Paramsukh do? Nothing. He tried again and again, but Nandishwar stayed where he was.

The merchant was thrilled!

"I knew it!" he shouted. "There is no bull in the world that can pull fifty loaded carts at a time. Come on; give me the thousand gold coins."

Poor Paramsukh had to hand over the gold coins without a word of protest, because he had lost the bet fair and square.

Sadly, he walked back home with Nandishwar and lay down on the bed and shut his eyes. All his dreams of becoming the richest man had been destroyed.

"What is the matter, master?" asked Nandishwar.

"What do you mean by asking me that question?" shouted Paramsukh. "All because of you I am ruined. I should never have listened to your silly suggestion."

"Why did you shout at me?" asked Nandishwar, "Why did you use the whip on me? You have never treated me like that before."

Paramsukh was quiet for some time. Then he said, "Yes, that was a mistake, I admit. Now just leave me alone to think."

Nandishwar walked back to his shed. He felt sorry for his master.
At least, his master had realised he had made a mistake. That was a good
sign. He went back to Paramsukh and said, "Let us forget about what
has happened. Now, go and bet again. But this time, place a bet for two
thousand gold coins, not just one thousand. And also remember not to be
rude and angry with me."

Paramsukh nodded. When he told the merchant about the second bet, the merchant started laughing.

"So you want to lose again?" he mocked.

"No," said Paramsukh, "I am sure of winning this time."

"Very well," said the merchant, eager to win twice the number of gold coins.

Again that evening Paramsukh tied the yoke on Nandishwar's neck with the fifty carts behind him. Then he sat on the first cart and gently said, "Come on, son. Let us win this bet together. I know you can do it."

This time Nandishwar did not let his master down. He pulled the carts with ease. The merchant could not believe his eyes!

"Your bull is the strongest I have ever seen," he said, "You deserve to win the two thousand gold coins. Here, take it."

Paramsukh took the coins and walked home with his bull happily, having learnt a very important lesson.